SHARE A STORY

The Big Wide-Mouthed Frog

Introduction

One of the best ways you can help
your children learn and learn to read
is to share books with them. Here's why:

• They get to know the **sounds**, **rhythms** and **words**
used in the way we write. This is different from how we
talk, so hearing stories helps children learn how to read.

• They think about the **feelings** of the characters
in the book. This helps them as they go about
their own lives with other people.

• They think about the **ideas** in the book. This helps
them to understand the world.

• Sharing books and listening to what your children
say about them shows your children that you care
about them, you care about what they think
and who they are.

Michael Rosen

Michael Rosen
Writer and Poet
Children's Laureate (2007-9)

For Andrés

First published 1999 by Walker Books Ltd
87 Vauxhall Walk, London SE11 5HJ

This edition published 2011

2 4 6 8 10 9 7 5 3 1

Text © 1999 Walker Books Ltd
Illustrations © 1999 Ana Martín Larrañaga
Concluding notes © CLPE 2011

The right of Ana Martín Larrañaga to be identified as illustrator of this work
has been asserted by her in accordance with the Copyright, Designs and Patents Act 1988

This book has been typeset in ITC Highlander

Printed in China

British Library Cataloguing in Publication Data:
a catalogue record for this book is available from
the British Library

ISBN 978-1-4063-3492-0

www.walker.co.uk

The Big Wide-Mouthed Frog

A Traditional Tale

Illustrated by

Ana Martín Larrañaga

WALKER BOOKS

AND SUBSIDIARIES

LONDON · BOSTON · SYDNEY · AUCKLAND

Once there was a big
wide-mouthed frog with
the biggest, widest mouth
you ever did see.

And one day that big
wide-mouthed frog
hopped off to see
the world.

The first creature he met
had big thumping feet.

"Hey, you! Big Thumping Feet!
Who are you and what do you eat?"
shouted the wide-mouthed frog.
"I'm a kangaroo," said Kangaroo,
"and I eat grass."
"Well, I'm a big wide-mouthed frog!"
shouted the wide-mouthed frog.
"And I eat flies!"

The second creature
he met had a big
black nose.

"Listen, Mister Big Nose!
Who are you and what do you eat?"
shouted the wide-mouthed frog.

"I'm a koala," said Koala,
"and I eat leaves."
"Well, I'm a big wide-mouthed frog!"
shouted the wide-mouthed frog.
"And I eat flies!"

The third
creature
he met was
hanging
upside down.

"Ho there,

Upside-down Creature!

Who are you and what do you eat?"

shouted the wide-mouthed frog.

"I'm a possum," said Possum,

"and I eat blossom."

"Well, I'm a big wide-mouthed frog!"

shouted the wide-mouthed frog.

"And I eat flies!"

The fourth creature he met
had three long toes.
"Look here, Three Long Toes!
Who are you and what do you eat?"
shouted the wide-mouthed frog.

"I'm an emu," said Emu,
"and I eat grasshoppers."
"Well, I'm a big wide-mouthed frog!"
shouted the wide-mouthed frog.
"And I eat flies!"

Then the wide-mouthed frog
met a creature stretched out
on the riverbank like a
knobbly brown log.

"HEY, Knobbly Brown Log!
Who are you and what do
you eat?" shouted the
wide-mouthed frog.

Knobbly Brown Log
opened her mouth
in a slow, wide,
lazy smile.

"Good-day to you, too," she said.
"I'm a crocodile and I eat big
wide-mouthed frogs. Who are
you and what do you eat?"

"Me?" whispered the wide-mouthed frog, puckering his mouth into the smallest, narrowest mouth you ever did see.

"I'm just a small narrow-mouthed frog and ...

Sharing Stories

Sharing stories together is a pleasurable way to help children learn to read and enjoy books. Reading stories aloud and encouraging children to talk about the pictures and join in with parts of the story they know well are good ways to build their interest in books. They will want to share their favourite books again and again. This is an important part of becoming a successful reader.

The Big Wide-Mouthed Frog is an amusing Australian traditional tale about a wide-mouthed frog that warns of the dangers of being "too big for your boots". Here are some ways you can share this book:

• Spending time talking together about the book – the story and pictures – is a good way for children to explore its meanings. This supports their understanding, as they can tell you anything that puzzles them and talk about their favourite part of the story.

• The repeated phrases help children to join in the reading of the story. Gradually they learn to match the words they say to those on the page.

• Each animal has its own personality. By reading aloud in a different voice for each one, you can make the story more meaningful, enjoyable and memorable. It's a good way to help children read expressively when they read for themselves.

• The story has a surprise ending which is funny and good to talk about. What do children think happened to the frog? Do they think he learned his lesson? Did they think of a different ending?

• Children will enjoy telling the story by moving like each animal, "speaking" the different voices of the characters and using the repeated phrases in the story.

• Play a "What am I?" game, taking it in turns to describe the features of an animal in the story for the other person to guess.

SHARE A STORY
A First Reading Programme
From Pre-school to School

Beginnings – 2 years+

Look Out, Suzy Goose — Petr Horáček

Walking Through the Jungle — Julie Lacome — Introduced by Michael Rosen

Hello, Goodbye — David Lloyd, Louise Voce — Introduced by Michael Rosen

TEN IN THE BED — Penny Dale — Introduced by Michael Rosen

THIS IS THE BEAR — Sarah Hayes, Helen Craig — Introduced by Michael Rosen

The Big Wide-Mouthed Frog — Ana Martín Larrañaga — Introduced by Michael Rosen

Early Steps – 3 years+

A New House for Mouse — Petr Horáček — Introduced by Michael Rosen

The Train Ride — June Crebbin, Stephen Lambert — Introduced by Michael Rosen

THE OTHER DAY I MET A BEAR — Russell Ayto — Introduced by Michael Rosen

Old MacDonald Had a Farm — Jane Chapman — Introduced by Michael Rosen

The Tiger and the Jackal — Vivian French, Alison Bartlett — Introduced by Michael Rosen

Zed's Bread — Mick Manning, Brita Granström — Introduced by Michael Rosen

Next Steps – 4 years+

The Hairy Toe — Daniel Postgate — Introduced by Michael Rosen

The True Story of Humpty Dumpty — Sarah Hayes, Charlotte Voake — Introduced by Michael Rosen

BEANS ON TOAST — Paul Dowling — Introduced by Michael Rosen

Over in the Meadow — A Counting Rhyme — Louise Voce — Introduced by Michael Rosen

Dog Blue — Polly Dunbar — Introduced by Michael Rosen

Night-night, Knight And Other Poems — Michael Rosen, Sue Heap — Introduced by Michael Rosen

Taking Off – 5 years+

"Have You Seen the Crocodile?" — Colin West — Introduced by Michael Rosen

HANDA'S SURPRISE — Eileen Browne — Introduced by Michael Rosen

The Ravenous Beast — Niamh Sharkey — Introduced by Michael Rosen

One, Two, Flea! — Allan Ahlberg, Colin McNaughton — Introduced by Michael Rosen

Dinosaurs' Day Out — Nick Sharratt — Introduced by Michael Rosen

The Old Woman and the Red Pumpkin — Betsy Bang, Rachel Merriman — Introduced by Michael Rosen

Sharing the best books makes the best readers

WALKER BOOKS

www.walker.co.uk